CHADRON (NE) STATE COLLEGE

3 5086 00336768 5

D1129793

Demco

DAN FRONTIER
WITH THE INDIANS

by
William Hurley

illustrations
Jack Boyd

BENEFIC PRESS • CHICAGO

PUBLISHING DIVISION OF BECKLEY-CARDY COMPANY

Chadron State College Library
Chadron, Nebraska

DAN FRONTIER

DAN FRONTIER AND THE NEW HOUSE

DAN FRONTIER GOES HUNTING

DAN FRONTIER AND THE BIG CAT

DAN FRONTIER WITH THE INDIANS

DAN FRONTIER, TRAPPER

DAN FRONTIER SCOUTS WITH THE ARMY

DAN FRONTIER AND THE WAGON TRAIN

DAN FRONTIER, SHERIFF

1962 Printing

Copyright 1959 by Benefic Press

All Rights Reserved

Printed in the United States of America

Library of Congress
Number 59-8828

+
H939i

Gift

INDEX

STORIES

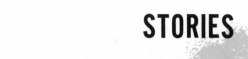

To the Salt Licks

This is Dan Frontier.
Dan lives in Kettle Creek.
Dan works in Kettle Creek.

Mr. and Mrs. Healy live
in Kettle Creek.
Kathy and Jimmy live here, too.
The Healys are friends
of Dan Frontier.

Dan went to see the Healys.

"We must go for some salt,"
Dan said to Mr. Healy.

"Soon we will have no salt.
We must have salt to eat
with meat."

"We must have salt to keep
the meat, too," said Mrs. Healy.
"And we must have salt
for other things."

"I will go now," said Dan.
"I will get some other men.
We will come back for you.
Then we will go to the licks
and get the salt."

Dan went away to find some other men.

He stopped here and there in Kettle Creek.

Soon Dan went back to the Healys with the men.

Mr. Healy was ready to go.

Away they went.

They went on and on.

"We must stop here," said Dan.

"We can not see now.

We will eat and sleep.

Then we will go on."

"Um-m-m-m, that was good,"
said Dan Frontier.

"Now we must get some sleep,"
said Mr. Healy.

"The men are ready for sleep."

"I will not sleep," Dan said.
"I will look out for Indians.
You and the others sleep."
"Soon I will get up, Dan,
and you can sleep," said Mr. Healy.

Soon the sun was up.

"Get up, men!" called Mr. Healy.

"It is time to eat and go."

The men got ready.

"Indians may come,"
said Dan.

"We must be ready."

Away they went.
They went on
and on.
Then Dan said,
"Look there!"

"See the salt
licks!" said Dan.
"I see the
salt licks,"
said Mr. Healy.

15

"Here we are,"
said Dan.
"This is called
Blue Licks.
The salt is
in this water."

"Come," said Dan Frontier.
"We must get to work now."
Some of the men made a fire.
Some got kettles of salt water.
Dan and Mr. Healy made
something for the kettles.

Soon the kettles were
over the fire.

"We will eat now," said Dan.

"And then we will look
in the kettles."

The men got ready to eat.

Soon it was time to look
in the kettles.
"Look!" called Mr. Healy.
"Look in the kettles.
There is no water now.
There is salt."

"Good!" said Dan Frontier.

"Now, the salt will go into bags."

The men worked and worked
with the bags of salt.

Then Dan said, "We will get
some sleep now.

Then we can get more salt."

Indians Stop Dan

"Get up!" called Dan.

The men got up.

Then Dan said, "They need this salt in Kettle Creek.

King and I will get this salt to Kettle Creek."

"Come, King," Dan said
to his horse.

Dan got King ready to go.

Dan got the bags of salt
ready to go, too.

"Here we go!" Dan said.

"We are on the way now.

You must help me get this salt
to Kettle Creek."

Away went King and Dan.

They went on and on.

The wind came up.

Dan did not like the wind.

King did not like the wind.

"I can not see far.

But we must go on," said Dan.

"They need this salt

in Kettle Creek."

"King, stop!" called Dan.

"I see something!"

Dan looked and looked.

"I see Indians over there,"
Dan Frontier said.

"They must not see you and me."

"We will stop here," said Dan.
"The Indians will go away.
Then we can get away."
Dan looked and looked.
Then Dan said, "Now, King,
we can go on!"

But something stopped Dan.
"Uh-h-h-h!" said Dan Frontier.
"Let go of me!"
"No!" said a big Indian.
"Brave Eagle take you
to Chief Black Fish.
Brave Eagle take the horses.
Brave Eagle take the salt."

Then Brave Eagle called
more Indians to come.

They helped get Dan's horses.

"You look like Dan Frontier,"
one Indian said.

"I am, I am!" said Dan.

"Let me go now!"

"No!" said Brave Eagle.

"We take you to Black Fish."

Soon Dan saw Chief Black Fish.
"We find Dan Frontier,"
Brave Eagle said.
"We find Dan Frontier in land
of Chief Black Fish."

"Dan Frontier!"
said Chief Black Fish.
"You are friend of Black Fish."

"We take your salt.
We take your horses.
But we will not hurt you,"
Chief Black Fish said.
"You are friend of my men."

"Chief Black Fish, you are
my friend, too," said Dan.

"Now will you let me go
to Kettle Creek?"

"No!" said Chief Black Fish.

"You come to my land.

You can not go from my land."

Then Chief Black Fish and his men
went away to talk.

"What will Chief
Black Fish and
the Indians do
with me now?"
thought Dan.

Son of Black Fish

Black Fish and
his men talked.
Then Black
Fish said, "Dan
Frontier will be
my son."

"Dan Frontier
will be called
Big Turtle.
Go, get Big
Turtle," said
Black Fish.
"I will talk
with him."

"You are my son now,"
said Chief Black Fish.

"You are Big Turtle, son
of Black Fish.

You will live here.

You will hunt with my men.

You will work with my men.

Big Turtle will like it here."

Then Black Fish went away.

Dan thought, "I will be
the son of Chief Black Fish.

I will hunt with the Indians.

I will work with the Indians.

But some day I will get away
from Chief Black Fish.

I will go back to Kettle Creek."

Dan worked.

Dan hunted.

Dan played, too.

Chief Black Fish said,
"My son, you are a good hunter.
This time you will hunt
with me.
Come, Big Turtle."
Dan and Black Fish went
away to hunt.

"Look up!" called Dan.

ZING!

"I got one!" called Black Fish.

ZING!

"I got one, too," called Dan.

Dan and Black Fish went on.
They got more birds.
Black Fish said, "I like
to hunt with you, Big Turtle.
We will hunt other times, too."

Black Fish
and Dan Frontier
went back.
"This will be
good to eat,"
said Black Fish.

Hunters From Kettle Creek

One night Dan saw Indians run
to Chief Black Fish.

They said to Black Fish,
"Men from Kettle Creek come!

They hunt in land of
Black Fish!

They get birds of Black Fish!"

Black Fish
called many
Indians to come
to him.
They talked
and talked.

Dan thought, "What will
Black Fish's men do?
They do not like hunters
from Kettle Creek in this land.
Maybe the Indians will go
to Kettle Creek and fight."
Dan thought and thought.
Then he went to sleep.

Dan got up.
He saw Indians here.
He saw Indians there.
The Indians worked and worked.
They worked fast.
Dan thought, "What are
the Indians going to do?"

That night Dan saw
a big, big fire.

He saw Indians dance
and dance.

"Soon the Indians will be
ready to fight," thought Dan.

"Will they go to Kettle Creek?"

"I must find
out," said Dan.
"I will go to
Black Fish."
Dan went away
from the fire.
He went to see
Black Fish.

"There is a big fire
out there," Dan said.
"Your men dance and dance.
What are your men going
to do, Black Fish?"

"Men of Kettle Creek come," said Black Fish.

"Men of Kettle Creek hunt in the land of Black Fish.

Black Fish's men do not like hunters here.

Black Fish's men dance.

Black Fish's men get ready for big fight."

"Let me go to Kettle Creek,"
said Dan Frontier.
"I will tell the men there
not to hunt in your land."
"No!" said Chief Black Fish.
"You can not go, Big Turtle.
Men of Black Fish will go
to Kettle Creek to fight."

Dan went away.

He thought and thought.

"I must get away from here.

I must get to Kettle Creek.

I have friends there.

The Healys are in Kettle Creek.

The Indians may hurt the Healys."

Dan did not go back to look
at the dances now.

He went to sleep.

Soon the sun was up.

Many Indians were up, too.

They worked and worked
to make a big fire.

That night there were
more dances.

Chadron State College Library
Chadron, Nebraska

Dan looked and looked
at the big fire and the dances.
"Now is the time for me
to get away," thought Dan Frontier.
"But I must find King.
King must help me get away
to Kettle Creek."

"Stop!" called Brave Eagle.
"Where do you go, Big Turtle?"
Dan thought fast.
"I can not fight the men
of Kettle Creek," said Dan.
"I can not be in the dance.
I am going to sleep now."

"I can not
get away now,"
thought Dan.

"I said I was
going to sleep.

I must go to
sleep then.

But there will
be other nights
and more dances.

Then I will
get away from
Black Fish and
his men."

There were more fires.

And there were more dances.

One night, Dan thought,
"Now is a good time for me
to look for King.

This is the time for me
to get away."

Dan looked here.

Dan looked there.

Then he went away
from the fire.

He went to look for King.

"There he is!" said Dan.

"Sh-h-h-h, King!

We must get away now!"

"Do not run now," said Dan.
"The Indians will hear you.
But you can run soon, King!
You can run on the way
to Kettle Creek."

"Now, King," said Dan Frontier.
"Run! Run! Run!"
King went fast.
"I can not see," said Dan.
"You must help me find the way
to Kettle Creek.
Soon the Indians will go
to Kettle Creek.
There may be a big fight."

The wind was cold.

Dan and King went on and on.

Dan wanted to sleep.

Dan wanted to eat.

But he did not stop.

Then Dan saw the sun.

"Look, King!"
said Dan.
"I can see
Kettle Creek.
Run fast, King," said Dan.
On went Dan Frontier and King.
Soon they were in Kettle Creek.

Kettle Creek Gets Ready

Dan went to the Healys.

"Dan, it is good to see you!"
Mr. Healy said.

"We looked and looked for you.

We did not like to come back
without you.

But the people needed the salt."

"Are you hurt?" said Jimmy.
"No," said Dan Frontier.
"The Indians got me.
They got my salt and horses, too.
Then the Indians made me go
to Chief Black Fish."

Dan Frontier said, "I wanted
to come back to Kettle Creek.
But Black Fish said no.
He said I was his son.
He said I was to live there
in the land of Black Fish."

Then Dan said, "One time
the Indians saw hunters.
They were from Kettle Creek.
Black Fish did not like men
from Kettle Creek in his land.
The Indians made a big fire.
The Indians danced and danced.
They got ready for a big fight."

"One night the Indians danced
on and on.

That was the night I got away.

I came to Kettle Creek fast.

The Indians will dance more.

But soon the dances will stop.

Then the Indians will come here
to fight.

We must get ready now."

"The Indians will hurt you.
They will take your horses,
too," Dan Frontier said.

"Come," Dan said
to Mr. Healy.
"We must get
some men to help
make a big wall.
The wall will
help to keep out
the Indians."

Dan said, "We may have to live inside the wall for a long time.

The Indians may not go away.

Jimmy, you will help the men hunt for meat to eat.

Mrs. Healy, will you and Kathy get things ready, too?"

Some men worked and worked
on the big wall.

Some other men hunted.

Jimmy hunted with the men.

They got many birds to eat.

Mrs. Healy and Kathy helped
to get water and other things.

Soon the big wall was ready.
Mrs. Healy and Kathy came
with water and many things.
Jimmy and the hunters came
with meat.

Then Dan Frontier called out,
"Now come here!
Get inside the big wall.
Get the horses inside, too.
We are ready for the Indians."

"We all need sleep.

But some of you will not get
to sleep now," said Dan.

"You must help me look out
for Indians.

Then you can sleep and some
of the others can get up."

Then Dan said good-night.

The sun came up.

Dan and Mr. Healy called,
"Get up! Get up!"

Jimmy helped to make a fire.

Mrs. Healy and Kathy helped
get things ready to eat.

Then a man
called, "Let me in!"
"Let him in,"
Dan called down
to one of his men.
"He went out
to see if Indians
were on their way
to Kettle Creek."
"I saw Indians
not too far from
here!" the man said
to Dan Frontier.

"Get your guns ready!"
called Dan to the other men.
"Black Fish and his men are
on their way here."

Soon Dan said,
"I see Black
Fish and his
men over there.
Do not fire
your guns now.
We will see
what the Indians
are going to do."

The Indians saw the wall.
They did not like it.
Then the Indians went away
from the big wall.

"What are the Indians going
to do now?" said Jimmy.

"They are going away," said Dan.
"But they will not go far."

"Soon the Indians will do
something," said Dan.
"Look out, men!
Fire! Fire! Fire!"

"What can we do now, Dan?"
said Mr. Healy.

"Soon there will be more fires."

Dan said, "Have Jimmy and some
of the men put out the fires.

There is water inside the wall
to put out the fires.

The other men must help you
and me fight the Indians."

Jimmy and some others worked
and worked to put out the fires.
"Men!" called Dan Frontier.
"The Indians will not stop.
I must go out to Black Fish.
I must stop this fight.
We can not have more fires
inside this wall."

"No! No!" called the men.

"You will be hurt,"
said Mr. Healy.

"One time I was the son
of Black Fish," said Dan.

"Maybe he will talk to me.
I must go out and see.
I do not want the Indians
to hurt you."

Then Dan got
up on the wall.
He looked for
Chief Black Fish.

Soon Dan saw
Chief Black Fish.
Dan called to him,
"Chief Black Fish!
This is Big Turtle,
the son of Chief
Black Fish.
Do you hear me?"

83

"I want to talk to you,"
Dan said to Chief Black Fish.
"Have your men get back."

Chief Black Fish said, "Men
of Kettle Creek put guns away.
Then men of Black Fish get back."
Dan talked to his men.
Dan saw Black Fish talk
to his men, too.
He saw the Indians back away.

"You must come away from wall,"
Chief Black Fish called.
"Then I talk to Big Turtle."
Dan went away from the wall.

"Chief Black Fish, one time
I was your son," Dan said.

"You called me Big Turtle.
I lived with you.
I hunted with you.
Do you want to hurt me
and my men?"

"I do not want to hurt you,"
said Chief Black Fish.

"But men of Black Fish want
to fight.

They do not like other men
of Kettle Creek.

Men of Kettle Creek hunt
in the land of Black Fish."

"Black Fish, stop the fight
and go away," said Dan.
"Then I will do this for you.
I will see that my men
from Kettle Creek do not hunt
in the land of Black Fish.
Take your men away now.
We will let you have some meat.
We will be your friends."

Black Fish
went back to
see his men.

Black Fish and
his men talked
and talked.

Then Black Fish
came back to
see Dan Frontier.

Chief Black Fish said,
"Black Fish want to be friend.
Black Fish stop fight now.
My men will take your meat.
Then we will go away."

Dan went back to his men.
"The fight is over!" called Dan.

"Dan, you came back!
You were not hurt!" said Jimmy.
"Dan Frontier made friends
with the Indians," said Mr. Healy.
"Dan stopped the fight
and helped Kettle Creek!"

VOCABULARY

The total vocabulary of this book is 131 words. Of these, 22 are first-grade words; 11 are above first grade; and the rest are below first grade. First-grade words are listed in roman type, and those above first grade are in italics. The words are listed in alphabetical order, and the numbers indicate the pages on which the words first appear.

bags 20

cold 59

dance 45

far 23
fight 43
fire 17
friends 6

guns 75

hear 57
horse 22

hunt 34
hunter 37
hurt 30

if 74
Indians 13
inside 68

keep 8
kettles 17

land 28
licks 5
long 68

many 42
meat 7
men 9
more 20

need 21

other 8

salt 5
son 33

talk 32
thought 32

wall 67
wind 23

DEVELOPMENT OF READING SKILLS

Reading is an important skill integral in learning any subject area. The prerequisite for effective use of reading material is interest. If the child has genuine interest in content, the exercise of reading skills becomes meaningful and enables him to transfer these skills to basic books in any subject.

The supplementary reader provides, in a high-interest story, the exercise and development of reading skills learned in the basic reader.

THE READING SKILLS
I Promoting Growth in Interpretative Skills

Interpreting the main idea

A strong and fast-moving plot is built around the capture of Dan Frontier by the Indians and Dan's later escape to save Kettle Creek. This plot is clearly portrayed on pp. 26, 28, 31, 34-35, 49-50, 52-56, 60, 65, 67. *27, 32, 33, 57-59, 81, 92-93.

Comprehending phrase and sentence meanings

Clear narrative writing helps the reader to understand fully a situation, a scene of action, or a characterization. Note narration on pp. 17 and 44, which describes scenes of activity. *5-6, 10, 23.

Observing details and understanding their relationship

A plot is strengthened if significant details relative to the main idea are written into the story at strategic points. Note the importance of the details on p. 41. These details serve to introduce the Indians' preparation for war on Kettle Creek on pp. 44, 45, 48 and 51, Dan's escape on pp. 55-58, and Dan's saving Kettle Creek from the Indians on pp. 67, 81-93.

Interpreting a story in sequence

A chain of logically planned events in a story shows the child how certain happenings result in a related action. On p. 8 the people of Kettle Creek need salt. This leads to Dan's trip to the licks. On p. 26 Dan is captured. On p. 48 Kettle Creek is endangered, which leads to the battle on p. 79 and the outcome of the story on p. 91.

Making inferences

Children will learn to read more intelligently and with more enjoyment if they are given an opportunity to make inferences. On p. 21 Dan sets out alone carrying salt for Kettle Creek. The child can infer from this that Dan is brave and will assume the lead in a time of danger. *65.

Forming associations

Children will be able to follow the plot more easily if they can form proper associations. Because of the dress and customs of the story characters and of the appearance of the terrain, the child will associate the story with the proper time and place—the early frontier. *5-7, 12 and 13, 26, 38 and 39, 60.

Forming sensory images

To be able to feel or visualize experiences of the story characters is a necessity if a child is going to find real meaning and interest in his reading. On p. 50 the child will, no doubt, experience worry, anxiety, and sadness just as Dan does when he realizes his friends may be in great danger. *12, 23, 59.

Anticipating outcomes

If the child reads carefully and observes details, he will be able to anticipate outcomes of the story. On p. 26 Dan is outnumbered and caught by the Indians. What can he do? On p. 54 Dan has to get away. How will he do it? *81, 82, 89.

Making judgments and drawing conclusions

If a child is comprehending what he is reading and is relating the pictures to the reading matter, he will be able to make intelligent judgments and conclusions. On p. 12 the reader will conclude that the men have been riding all day and are very tired from a long trip. 87.

Strengthening memory by observation, association, and visual imagery

The child must remember certain descriptions and details relative to the main theme of the story in order to follow the plot intelligently. Note how the following pages emphasize that Dan lives in and has friends in Kettle Creek: pp. 4-6, 10, 21, 23, 31, 35, 49, 50. *52, 58, 60, 61, 63, 65, 89.

II Promoting Growth in Word-Perception Skills

Establishing habits of viewing words in left to right serial order

The left-to-right movement is a basic skill in reading. By studying words that begin with the same initial blend but end differently and words that begin and end with the same letter but use a different middle letter the child can increase both his reading skill and his skill in word-identification. Note "they" and "then" on p. 11 and "got" and "get" on p. 14. *12, 13, 15, 17, 21, 34, 51.

Observing individual words or phrases in context

Recognition of words and phrases and the understanding of their meaning in relation to contextual material is of primary importance in gaining skill in reading. Note the use of the word "fire" on p. 18 and again on p. 76. *34.

Strengthening memory of word forms based on association of meaning with printed words, careful observation of visual details and visual imagery of words

Through association with the printed material and accompanying art work on pp. 9, 15-16, the children will learn a new conception of the word "licks."

Using meaningful clues as an aid in identifying words

Story sequence and skillful repetition are means of identifying words. On p. 7 the word "salt" is first used in a sentence. The picture and the context help to identify this word. "Salt" is also repeated on pp. 8, 9, 15, 16. *19-23, 26, 30, 62.

Developing phonetic skills, auditory perception of rhyme, visual auditory perception of rhyme, auditory perception of initial consonant sounds, substitution of initial consonants and auditory imagery

Use phonetic helps to further develop the child's ability to hear a word and to sound out a word. Note the words "eat," and "meat," on p. 7. Also note the difference in the sound of the letter "a" in the words "was" and "Dan" on p. 10. *52.

Developing structural analysis skills . . . recognition of words formed by adding "s" to known root words and recognition of compound words made up of two known root words

A vocabulary can be increased in several ways. Among these are learning to add "s" to known words and learning the compound forms of known words. Note "other" on p. 8 and "others" on p. 13. Note the words "some" on p. 7 and "things" on p. 8. The compound form of these words is found on p. 17.

Identifying words in capitalized and uncapitalized initial-letter forms

Have the children identify initial letters as they appear in capitals and lower-case forms. This will permit them to begin sentences with more ease. Note the word "look" on p. 19 and the word "fire" on pp. 76 and 80.

Testing mastery of sight vocabulary

Children may be overly dependent on contextual clues for identification of words. Additional practice with words out of context may aid the child in mastering an enriched sight vocabulary. Go back over words of similar construction such as "come," "some," and "home;" "go" and "so;" "fight" and "night."

III Promoting Growth in Language

Understanding that a sentence is a meaning unit

The way in which a particular word or group of words is used in a sentence determines the over-all meaning of the sentence. The same word or group of words might be used differently in another sentence. On p. 8 the reader will find a new connotation of the word "keep."

Enriching oral vocabulary

After reading the story the child should have a broader knowledge of word meanings and this should carry over to his oral vocabulary. For example, the children probably did not think of a salt lick as a source of salt for food.

* Additional material which will help in developing this reading skill through story material may be found on the following pages: